ARE YOU ONE OF DUNAGIN'S PEOPLE?

If you're beset by the cost of food, the energy crisis, polluted air, and the vagaries of the postal system—laughter can keep you sane. Try some; you'll feel better!

BY DUNAGIN

TEMPO
BOOKS

GROSSET & DUNLAP, INC.
Publishers • New York

"SOMEDAY ALL THIS WILL BE YOURS——
WHETHER YOU WANT IT OR NOT."

"ACUPUNCTURE? NEVER HEARD OF IT."

"THIS ASSIGNMENT IS OF THE UTMOST URGENCY, HENRY. I WANT YOU TO LEAVE IMMEDIATELY— IN THE NEXT CARPOOL!"

"SOMETHING'S UP. I HEAR KISSINGER IS PLANNING A TRIP TO WASHINGTON."

7-1

11-16
Publishers-Hall Syndicate

Dunagin
© 1971 Orlando Sentinel

"WE'VE CERTAINLY GOT THE WORLD WONDERING
WHAT'S GOING ON HERE IN CHINA———
I WONDER WHAT IS GOING ON.."

"...AND WELCOME TO ANOTHER FIRESIDE CHAT ON THE FUEL SHORTAGE."

"LET'S CHANGE FORMATION AGAIN AND GIVE
'EM ANOTHER UFO SCARE."

"NO, I HAVEN'T HEARD ABOUT THE OIL SHORTAGE — TELL ME ABOUT IT!"

"THEY MUST BE USING THE INTERSTATE ROUTE."

6-2

"I WISH THERE WAS A WAY TO MAKE OUR SIGN LESS VISIBLE FROM THE HIGHWAY."

7-15

© 1971 Orlando Sentinel

Publishers-Hall Syndicate

"DON'T LOOK NOW, BUT IS THAT RALPH
NADER BACK THERE?"

"HOW'S THAT FOR A QUIET RIDE? WITH THE WINDOWS ROLLED UP, YOU CAN HARDLY HEAR THE SCREAMS OF THE ENVIRONMENTAL PROTECTION AGENCY."

"SORRY, WE CAN'T GIVE YOU THE MEAT PRICES UNLESS THERE'S A DOCTOR PRESENT."

"WELL, I CAN'T ALLOW YOU MUCH ON IT."

"I'M A FAILURE, WALTER. MY OFFICE HAS NEVER BEEN BUGGED."

" TAKE A MEMO, MISS WATSON. TO JACK ANDERSON...
JUST SEND IT ANYWHERE — HE'LL GET IT..."

"OUR WITNESS AGREES TO TESTIFY ON WATER-
GATE IN EXCHANGE FOR LIMITED IMMUNITY
AND THE MOVIE RIGHTS."

"I'M SEARCHING FOR AN UNIMPEACHABLE SOURCE."

1-15

© 1970 Orlando Sentinel
Publishers-Hall Syndicate

"NO COMMENT."

"WHY, IT'S A LITTLE TAPE RECORDING OF THE ROAR OF THE SURF."

"YESSIR, I'M NEW AROUND HERE. ISN'T EVERYONE?"

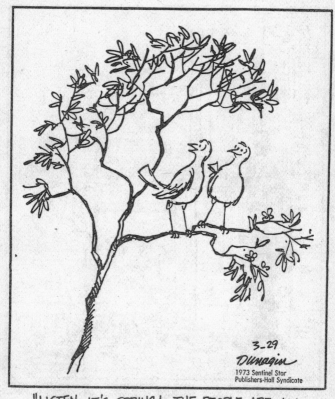

3-29

Dunagin

1973 Sentinel Star
Publishers-Hall Syndicate

"LISTEN, IT'S SPRING! THE PEOPLE ARE ALL SCREAMING ABOUT THEIR INCOME TAX."

INCOME TAX
ADVICE:
PAY IT

1040
N MAIN

3-8

Dunagin.

© 1972 Orlando Sentinel
Publishers-Hall Syndicate

"MULTIPLY TOTAL NUMBER OF EXEMPTIONS CLAIMED ON LINE 10 BY $750...."

"THE HIJACKER SAYS IT STARTED OUT AS AN ANTI-IMPERIALIST GESTURE. HE'S WILLING TO GIVE CAPITALISM A CHANCE, HOWEVER, SO HE'S DEMANDING $200,000."

"SURE I KNOW WHAT H²O MEANS — TWO PARTS HYDROGEN AND ONE PART OIL."

4-18

" 'I'M MAROONED ON A TROPICAL ISLAND WITH NO TAXES, POLLUTION, OR TRAFFIC...EAT YOUR HEARTS OUT."

6-29

Dunagin

"GASP! HELP!"

4-13

© 1971 Orlando Sentinel
Publishers-Hall Syndicate

"JUST ONE LAST ATTEMPT TO LAND THE
SUPPORT OF THE AUDUBON SOCIETY."

8-14

Dunagin

© 1970 Orlando Sentinel
Publishers-Hall Syndicate

"ON A CLEAR DAY YOU CAN SEE
THE SMOG IN THREE STATES."

6-30

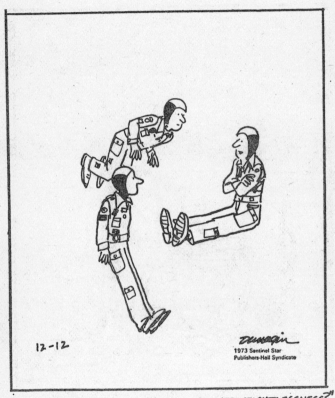

12-12

Dunagin

1973 Sentinel Star
Publishers-Hall Syndicate

"IS THERE SUCH A THING AS OVERWEIGHTLESSNESS?"

"SOMETHING TELLS ME WE'D BETTER WIN
THIS ONE, BOY."

COMPLETE
INCOME TAX
SERVICE
WE CRY FOR YOU

1-15

© 1971 Orlando Sentinel
Publishers-Hall Syndicate

"I EVEN REMINDED MY DAD I WAS EIGHTEEN AND ELIGIBLE TO VOTE — UNFORTUNATELY HE ISN'T RUNNING FOR ANYTHING."

"DARLING, YOUR ITSY-BITSY LOVEY-DOVEY DOLL HAS BEEN RECALLED BY THE FDA."

"I'VE BEEN LOOKING FOR THAT FOR TWO MONTHS!"

"MAKE THAT MR. AND <u>MS.</u>, DEAR."

4-7

"YOUR FIRST X-RATED MOVIE?"

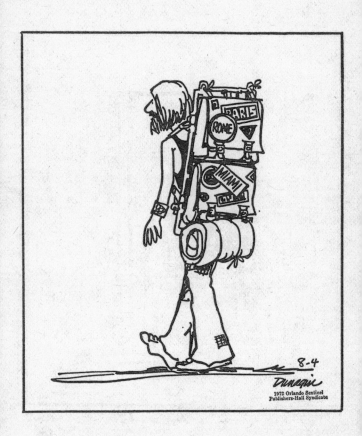

8-4

1972 Orlando Sentinel
Publishers-Hall Syndicate

"THIS IS A VERY CONTROVERSIAL FILM. THE CRITICS CAN'T DECIDE WHETHER IT'S PORNOGRAPHY OR DIRTY ART."

"THE BEST ACTOR AWARD GOES TO LAWRENCE RIPLEY!—FOR HIS PERFORMANCE IN ACCEPTING LAST YEAR'S BEST COSTUME DESIGN AWARD!"

1-27 © 1971 Orlando Sentinel
Publishers-Hall Syndicate

"NOT ONLY DOES YOUR STORY HAVE NO REDEEMING
SOCIAL VALUE, MR. HEMMINGWELL, IT ISN'T EVEN DIRTY."

"AND NOW A MESSAGE FROM OUR SPONSOR, FOLLOWED BY REASONS WHY YOU SHOULDN'T BELIEVE A WORD OF IT."

"I JUST HAD THE GREAT AMERICAN DREAM!"

8-19
Publishers-Hall Syndicate

Dunagin
© 1971 Orlando Sentinel

"HE SAYS THEY'VE NEVER HEARD OF WAR. THAT'LL
GIVE YOU AN IDEA HOW UNCIVILIZED THEY ARE."

"YOURS IS A PROBLEM COMMON IN TODAY'S COMPLEX SOCIETY —— YOU'RE NUTS."

Orlando Sentinel 1973
Publishers-Hall Syndicate

"THEY'RE TRYING TO KEEP THE MARIJUANA HARVEST DOWN THIS YEAR."

"AIN'T FOUND ANY GOLD, BUT THESE PANS REALLY COME CLEAN WITH ALL THAT DETERGENT IN THE WATER."

"NO WIFE OF MINE IS GOING TO SPEND MOTHER'S DAY IN THE KITCHEN. USE THE OUTDOOR GRILL."

"MRS. FINLEY, CAN JERRY COME OUT AND VOTE?"

"WE HAVE THE LAB REPORT ON THAT ORANGE SOIL THE GUYS FOUND ON THE MOON. IT'S TANG."

Orlando Sentinel
Publishers-Hall Syndicate

9-3

Dunagin

"IT SEEMS TO BE POWERED BY THAT GUY
ON THE BICYCLE."

7-23

©1969 Orlando Sentinel
Publishers-Hall Syndicate

"HELLO, MISSION CONTROL?"

1-8

"IF YOU THINK A LOT OF MONEY CHANGED HANDS BEFORE, JUST WAIT UNTIL YOU GET THE BILL FROM A _REAL_ PLUMBER."

"YOU'RE RIGHT — A DOLLAR JUST DOESN'T BUY WHOM IT USED TO."

5-7

U.S. POST OFFICE

STAMPS

FINANCING

5-21

"THIS IS SERIOUS, GENTLEMEN. SUPPOSE THE CONSUMER STOPPED BUYING <u>EVERYTHING</u> HE COULDN'T AFFORD!"

"RALPH NADER ISN'T GOING TO LIKE IT."

"TIME, 10:53 — 46 DEGREES —PARTLY CLOUDY—
AT THE TONE THE INTEREST RATE WILL BE..."

2-3

"HE SAYS HE'S FROM THE WAR ON
INFLATION, AND HE WANTS TO SURRENDER."

1-19

Orlando Sentinel
Publishers-Hall Syndicate

"WE MIGHT AS WELL FACE IT J.L. — IF THE ENERGY CRISIS BECOMES CRITICAL, WE MAY BE WALKING THIS COURSE SOMEDAY."

5-1

Dunagin

© 1971 Orlando Sentinel
Publishers-Hall Syndicate

"OUTBURSTS AND DISPLAYS OF TEMPER HAVE
NO PLACE IN LITTLE LEAGUE, TOMMY. IF IT HAPPENS
AGAIN, WE'LL HAVE TO ASK YOUR MOM TO LEAVE."

12-10

© 1970 Orlando Sentinel
Publishers-Hall Syndicate

"I'VE BEEN THINKING... ONLY A NUT WOULD PICK US
UP . AND WHO WANTS TO RIDE WITH A NUT?"

"LET'S SEE, I PUT THE DOGS IN THE KENNEL, STOPPED THE MAIL AND THE PAPER... DID WE FORGET ANYTHING, MARTHA? MARTHA?..."

6-16

© 1972 Orlando Sentinel

OPEN
SUNDAYS

12-11

©1969 Orlando Sentinel
Publishers-Hall Syndicate

"TO THE AIRPORT AND STEP ON IT! I HAVE
TO GET THERE IN TIME TO BE SEARCHED."

"YOUR TEETH ARE STRAIGHT, BUT WE HAVE
SOME STYLISH IMITATION BRACES..."

"I THINK MEMORIAL DAY IS WHEN WE HONOR
THOSE WHO GAVE US THE THREE-DAY WEEKEND."

5-28

1973 Sentinel Star
Publishers-Hall Syndicate

"I'VE HAD THREE OFFERS TO BUY MY OVERALLS."

2-17

© 1970 Orlando Sentinel
Publishers-Hall Syndicate

"I WAS AFRAID OF THIS! THEY'RE
JUST AS ADVANCED AS WE ARE."

1973 Sentinel Star
Publishers-Hall Syndicate

"WE CAN'T VERY WELL ASK THE CONSUMER TO CONSERVE FUEL IF WE AREN'T PREPARED TO PITCH IN, TOO, CAN WE?"

4-23

12-26

© 1970 Orlando Sentinel
Publishers-Hall Syndicate

"JOE, I'VE DECIDED TO TRADE YOU TO THE
THUNDERBOLTS FOR TWO OF YOUR FRANCHISE
HAMBURGER JOINTS."

"CAN WE GO OUTSIDE AND PLAY WITH THE AIR?"

"EVERYONE AROUND YOU IS GOING TO HAVE TO STOP SMOKING.

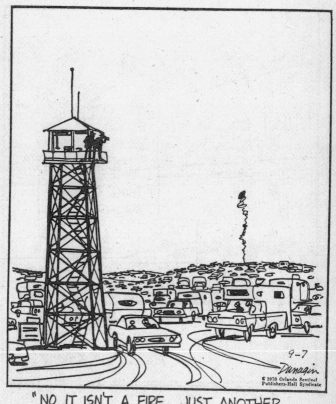

"NO, IT ISN'T A FIRE. JUST ANOTHER
RADIATOR BOILING OVER."

9-7

Dunagin

"DEAR, THERE'S A FORTY PERCENT CHANCE
I'LL BE LATE FOR DINNER."

"HERE'S YOUR $15,000 RECEIPT, DADDY."

"THIS STUFF IS PRETTY ADULT. ISN'T THERE
ANYTHING ON WITH SOME VIOLENCE IN IT?"

7-14

© 1971 Orlando Sentinel

Publishers-Hall Syndicate

"IF BUSINESS KEEPS UP LIKE THIS, R.J.,
THESE WILL BE THE GOOD OLD DAYS."

"GOING TO OR FROM THE FACTORY?"

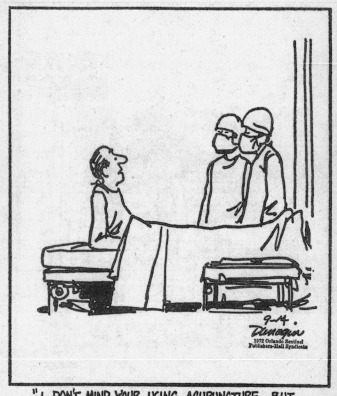

"I DON'T MIND YOUR USING ACUPUNCTURE, BUT
I WANT TO BE PUT TO SLEEP FIRST!"

"THE HEAVIER THIS PACK GETS, THE MORE
ANTI-MATERIALISTIC I BECOME."

THOU
SHALL
NOT
PARK

9-25
Publishers-Hall Syndicate

Dunagin
© 1971 Orlando Sentinel

5-15

© 1970 Orlando Sentinel
Publishers-Hall Syndicate

Dunagin

SCENIC
VIEW
20 MILES

MOTEL

7-16

Dunagin
© 1971 Orlando Sentinel

Publishers-Hall Syndicate

Sentinel Star

Publishers-Hall Syndicate

"NEW MATH GETS OLD, DOESN'T IT?"

"HEY, ISN'T THIS A VIOLATION OF THE SCHOOL'S DRESS CODE?"

"THIS IS THE TIME OF YEAR WHEN THE PLASTIC BAGS ALL FALL FROM THE TREES."

11-2 Dunagin

1972 Orlando Sentinel
Publishers-Hall Syndicate

"OH, GOODY! THIS IS WHERE THAT DENTIST
LIVES WHO ALWAYS GIVES US LOTS OF CANDY!"

10-31

DUNAGIN

1972 Orlando Sentinel
Publishers-Hall Syndicate

"THERE GO THE LIGHTS. THEY'VE EITHER JUST GONE TO BED OR THERE'S A POWER FAILURE."

9-22

© 1970 Orlando Sentinel
Publishers-Hall Syndicate

"I UNDERSTAND CROMWELL IS VERY
STRONG ON ECOLOGY."

11-22

Dunagin

"WELL, I'LL JUST PUT YOU DOWN AS 'UNDECIDED,' O.K.?"

WALL ST.

ONE WAY

5-19

—Dunagin

© 1970 Orlando Sentinel
Publishers-Hall Syndicate

"I WANT TO SEE MY LAWYER. HE'S IN
CELL 478."